G000268966

Published by Ad Hoc Fiction.
www.AdHocFiction.com

Purchasing Information:
Paperback available from www.AdHocFiction.com
E-book available from all usual outlets.

Printed in the UK.
First Printing 2021.

ISBN paperback 978-1-912095-06-3
ISBN e-Book 978-1-912095-05-6

The Yet Unknowing World

by

Fiona J. Mackintosh

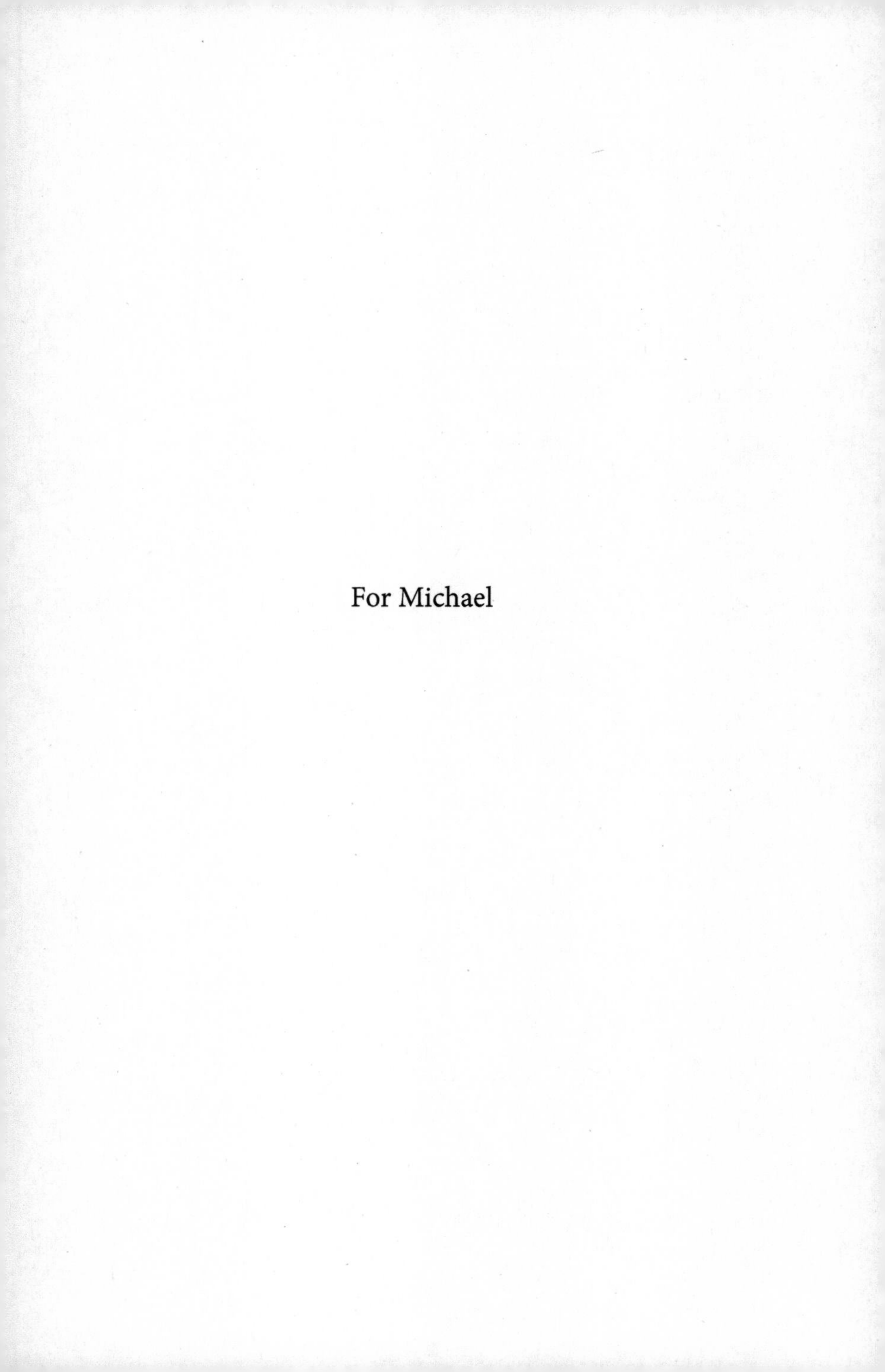

For Michael

And let me speak to the yet unknowing world
How these things came about: so shall you hear
Of carnal, bloody, and unnatural acts,
Of accidental judgments, casual slaughters,
Of deaths put on by cunning and forced cause,
And, in this upshot, purposes mistook
Fall'n on the inventors' reads: all this can I
Truly deliver.

Hamlet, Act V, Scene II

Contents

Old World

How It Begins

At first you don't pay much attention, just glancing at the headlines on the tram. It doesn't have a lot to do with you. The streets are clean, the shops are full, there's money in your pocket. You take your children to the park on Sunday afternoons to listen to the band. Your life is good, you don't ask why.

Sometimes the shattered glass and chalk marks on the walls make you feel uneasy, but you hurry home to hang your hat, the children milling round your legs, a juicy chicken waiting in the pot.

One night you hear cars braking in the silent street, boots on the stairs, a sharp rap on the door across the landing. You stand beside your own closed door to listen, fingering the safety chain, the children shushed, the baby at your wife's breast to stop her from whimpering. You hear a scuffling, dragging sound, then footsteps clatter down the stairs and engines rev away.

You'd always said to each his own, but now you have to wonder. They weren't too friendly when you'd see them on the stairs, eyes lowered, a mumbled word in passing. The man's long beard, the woman's headscarf tight around her face, the spicy smells that lingered in the building. Perhaps there is a need for rounding up and keeping track. There's your children's safety to consider after all. Where there's smoke, there must be fire, you say, and draw the bolts across your door.

The Last Encampment

Little Olive, 93, has a shock of white hair and skin the same shade as her name. She moves so fast with her walker that the nurses put an alarm pad on her mattress. Whenever it starts to wail, they come running to steer her back into bed. *This isn't much of a party,* Olive says. *No wonder the men didn't come.*

The ward is a hedge full of yattering birds. Belinda, large and Essex-feisty, kneads her hands in her lap and yells to no-one, *You're a right bloody head case! She ain't taking you back. I hope she jolly well dishes you.* In the bed across from hers, Noreen, tall and pink, has just turned 88. She's propped upright against the pillows, grumbling amid her cards and balloons. *Would you let me out please? I want to walk on these feet. Oh no, now my shoe has come undone. Why won't you help me?* In the next bay, Mavis sits on the side of her bed, combing her hair against the grain. As she tugs at the tangles, she murmurs her half of a conversation, pausing only to spit up mucus into a dish. As an orderly wheels a blood pressure machine down the ward, she hails him in a cut-glass voice, *I say, is it too late to get a gin and tonic?*

The blinds clatter in the thin breeze through the inched-open windows. Around the grey room, colour stabs the eye – floral curtains, orange plastic chairs, the bright red bins for waste. Machines beep and whirr, and lids bang as the staff take off their gloves and aprons. A telephone rings on and on at the nurses' station, and the rattle of wheels brings tea, meals, medicines ("Time for your tablets"), or just the ladies who mop the floors to mask the smell of piss and decay.

Yet when the nurses approach with washcloths and basins and whisk the curtains closed around the beds, the ward becomes a scatter of tents beside the sandstone rocks of Wadi Rum, and Mavis, Belinda, Noreen, and Olive are Bedouin queens with strong backs and hennaed fingers, their headdresses strung with dowry coins. In the last heat of the Saharan day, they drink camel's milk from goatskin bags and lift their heads to smell a haunch of meat roasting in the bone-dry desert air.

First Time

Friday night he's outside the chip shop with the lads, shoulders hunched against the east wind blowing off the sea. As she comes down the street laughing with another lassie, his palms grow damp. The lads caper, blethering in Monty Python voices, showing off. Soon her friend has a bus to catch, and the lads drift away, but she lingers. They share a bag of warm chips, hardly talking. He walks her home through the dark wynds, and up against an ancient wall, he turns to kiss her vinegar lips. Behind a listing headstone in the kirkyard, they struggle with zips and buttons, gasping and laughing when bare skin touches cold grass. Afterwards, he walks along the beach, slithering on the rocks in the dark. In sudden remembrance of the marvel of it, he stops in his tracks to bay his jubilation to the waxing moon.

Ice Harvesting

I'm in Sainsbury's frozen section looking at the ready meals when I see you. You're in the child seat of a trolley, holding onto the orange bar. The woman with you bends into the refrigerated case, and you stare at me over her back. I know that face. Your eyes are blue-grey, the pupils dark as slate. That arrow-straight hair, flyaway when brushed. It crackles and stands on end when I pull off your woolly hat and you run to the mirror, bent double with laughing.

I push my cart up behind yours. You lean sideways to look at me, the freezers enfolding us like an igloo. I want to reach out and zip up your jacket, though you never feel the cold. It only snowed once in your life. I called in sick, and we scraped enough together to make a squat ball which we squirted with the food colouring I'd used for your birthday cake.

The woman glances at me, then away. I follow you. It's warmer away from the freezers. I put random things in my cart – a jar of Taste the Difference curry sauce, an Easter egg in golden foil. When I lag behind, you look for me. You try to turn in the child seat, but your coat's too tight, and you let out a cry of annoyance.

Big red signs hang over our heads saying BUY 2 AND SAVE! ½ PRICE! 2 FOR £7.99! There were signs in the hospital too, huge blue ones with too many arrows – Radiology, Ultrasound, Acute Assessment, Pediatric Emergency. Chapel. Mortuary. Exit.

At the checkout the woman loads her shopping onto the belt, chatting with the girl at the till. You watch me from under those lashes I can still feel on the inside of my wrist. I could lean forward and touch the large round buttons on your coat. Our eyes are locked together as if our lives depended on it.

I leave my items on the belt and follow you outside. The till girl calls after me. A tepid rain is falling. You stare at me, one finger in your mouth, as the woman loads the orange bags into her 4 by 4. I hold tight to the trolley handle, adoring your head's perfect oval. An elderly man asks, "All right, pet?"

I smile.

"Fine thanks. Just thinking."

"Right you are then."

He touches a finger to the brim of his cap and limps away.

The car park is stained with damp. She's strapped you into your car seat, your moon face still turned towards me. I pull out my mobile, and, as the 4 by 4 reverses out of its space, I key in the license plate number and watch it dwindle into traffic.

You're gone, but I still feel your breath on my face, your heart in my chest. This is not like the last time. We'll be together again, my baby, my love. It won't be long at all.

How Gypsy Jenny Likes to Bathe

Lady Janet Anstruther floats on her back, her stomach rising from the water like the glossy hump of a whale. Each wave carries her closer to shore, but her strong arms keep her out beyond the rocks. The child eeling inside her is due by Whitsun, still two months away. After three boys and four sudden leachings of clots and fibre, she longs for a girl to walk with her on the sands of Ruby Bay at low tide, searching for sea garnets among the tangle.

She likes to brave the frigid waters as peeled as a newborn herself. As always, she sent a man with a handbell on ahead through the town to warn the locals. They think bodies are the devil's work but hate her for shielding them from the sight of hers. She's been cat-called Gypsy Jenny in the street for her sun-soaked skin. It's the price she pays for her good fortune, for the loving husband who had her portrait painted by the famous Reynolds, who built her a tower on the cliff facing her hometown across the firth. Yet she'd give up all the brocade gowns, the pearls, and the big stone house for one true companion who sees into her heart. She clasps her wet hands on her belly, feeling her daughter twist and kick, and imagines how they'll tread among the rocks and slick green weed, calling to each other as they cup the blood-red fragments in their palms.

Latchkey

"It's catch as catch can tonight," says Mum, easel under her arm, heading for her art class. She slaps the strewn newspapers for her keys. I look up from *Bleak House*.

"Supper?"

"A clever invention called sandwiches."

"Very droll, Mother."

"There's cheese. And lettuce."

She kisses Jerome's head. Finger's up his nose as usual.

"Later, bunnies. Don't set any fires."

The car door slams. I'm with Esther and Mr. Bucket galloping through the snow in search of Lady Dedham. I turn the pages faster under the lamp's circle. Just as Esther lifts the veil from the dead woman's face, I hear something.

"Jerome?"

Cellar door's open, steep steps vanish into darkness.

"I know you're down there."

No sound.

"Stop pretending this minute."

The silence is soupy, dense.

"I'm making supper. You better come."

Bread knife in hand, I lean the book against the toaster and step back into the black hole that yawns between the pages.

Agape

As we set off for Piraeus, the handsome cab driver folds his yellow cardigan neatly over the back of the passenger seat and taps his wedding ring to show us he's doing it to please his wife. I nod and smile and glance at you, but you've turned away, looking up at the shabby concrete buildings, bristling with television aerials and dipping lines of laundry.

We have to stop just beyond the Plaka for a funeral procession. People carry wreaths on long poles, dropping petals on the asphalt, and the driver catches my eye in the mirror. "Minister of Finance. Big guy." Through the open window, the sky's bedsheet-white scored with ancient columns. I breathe in petrol fumes and dust and watch the police hold hands to keep the crowd at bay.

There's a long delay at Piraeus. As the sun slowly sinks over the tangle of the city and the scrubby hills beyond, we follow other passengers onto another ferry, only to see the first one leave before ours, and I hear a woman laugh, "I guess we're on Greek time now." For five hours at sea on the windy deck, we sit apart in silence, wrapped in all the clothes we have.

It's too dark to read so I watch the moon trail on the ship's wake and strain above the engine's noise to hear the creak and splash of oars as the triremes of Athens keep pace beside us.

At midnight the ferry groans into Parikia, and the hotels flare into life like streetwalkers on the watch for sailors. They fire up again in the early hours to greet another ship, flooding our room with sudden light, and I see your back's turned against me in the narrow bed, the sheets thrashed around your legs.

Morning unfurls into sunshine, a dazzle of whitewash and Cyclades blue. Breakfast in the hotel café is hot chocolate dipped with almond bread, the tang of honeysuckle so strong it seeps in through the closed windows. Outside, the *meltemi* is sharp despite the sun, and I'm glad of my sweater. We walk through the crooked streets, past paint pots bursting with white geraniums, and, by a church with a red slate roof and a lemon tree hung with bells, we pause to watch the feral cats slumbering on the hot stones and you reach out at last and take my hand.

Hindsight

They cartwheel through his dreams, legs splayed, eyes open. Sometimes together, sometimes one at a time. Fabric unfurls around them, golds, blues, reds and greens. When he wakes, heart fractured, he can still see the colours on the back of his eyelids.

In the early morning darkness, he walks to the restaurant, his hands in his pockets, cracked from hours in the cold soapy water. He's left Tariq asleep on the mattress in the sitting room at his cousin's house. Later the boy will watch cartoons on TV and laugh. He's already forgetting his mother and sisters.

When the great wave came, he caught Tariq by the belt, but Meyra and the girls in their silky hijabs slid through his hands like fish. He still feels the boat buck and plunge beneath him as he walks, wishing now he'd pulled Tariq close and tipped them both backwards into the vast dark water.

Sole Survivor

The baby died after we'd walked about fifty miles out of the valleys. It was my turn to carry her, and I watched as her skin turned waxy. Dad sat on the verge, head in his hands, till Mum told him to dig. Igor twisted a berried branch from the hedge and stabbed it in the raw earth mound.

There was less to carry after that, though Andrey often rode on top of the cart, making it heavy for Dad and Igor to pull. The ground was claggy after the long, wet winter. Galina started dragging her feet, holding her stomach with her monthly pains. Outside Gloucester, she lay down and wouldn't get up. Sometimes I imagine she married a farmer in the Forest of Dean where the soil's rich in blood and marrow.

As we slept by a haystack on the road to Cirencester, soldiers smelling of liquor dragged Mum away. I clutched her leg, digging in my nails, but she slipped from my hands. In the dark, I heard Igor shout, a scuffle, then a single shot. In the watery dawn, the hole between his eyes was surprisingly small. The three of us wrapped what we could in bundles and left the cart behind.

South of Swindon we fell in with a convoy. Soldiers poked stragglers with rifles, rain streaming off their caps. I helped Andrey along, rubbing his back as he retched up sticky green phlegm. A medic in a sagging field tent tried to help, but with no supplies, he could do nothing for Andrey's lungs. He got Dad and me a lift on an Army jeep to Southampton. It was a long ride, cold and bumpy, but it saved our blistered feet and we were waved through every checkpoint.

At the DP camp, Dad smoked roll-ups behind the huts with other men, drinking moonshine from one tin cup. I latched onto another family. The mother was kind, but they left for America after a while. I'd wake in my bunk under the thin blanket, listening to the wind whistle through the gaps in the boards.

Every day I'd go to the far end of the camp to watch the big ships through the coils of barbed wire. That's where I met Peter, kicking an old boot sole around. Families got precedence for emigrating so we decided to marry and, by the time our papers came, I was expecting your mother. On the day we shipped, I didn't try very hard to find my Dad to say goodbye.

So that's my answer, child. I don't think back very often. It's you who matter – you, your brother and sister. But I do dream about them sometimes in the farmhouse, the baby banging on the kitchen table, Andrey mending his catapult, Galina helping Mum wash the pots, Dad and Igor cleaning the guns. And me up the valley in the dusk setting traps for rabbits as the rattle of gunfire echoes from the captured hills.

Reign

She gasps awake from dreams of bells tolling and a burst of ravens flapping skyward. The fire's dying, and across the room Margot stirs and murmurs in dreams of her own.

All day long, people whisked down long corridors, the telephone jangling. She and Margot played in the December gardens, galloping across the lawn, their breath trailing in clouds, while grown-ups paced behind the drawing room windows.

A rectangle of light and Mother's here, finger on her lips. The mattress sags as she sits. Her voice sounds different, like there's a twist in her throat.

"Well, darling, it's happened. Your father's to be King. Our lives are going to change, especially yours."

In the firelight, long shadows race up the walls like monkeys, hanging from looping branches, leering and clamouring. Lying very still, the young Elizabeth tries in vain to calm the manic jitter of her heart.

The Cardboard Box of Happiness

That day when you see them through the restaurant window, the sky is a hazy blue and the air in your throat is sweet and fresh, exams are over, *at last!* and walking is a rapture that lingers in the muscles of your stride, *happy!* and in just one breath, you've dropped your guard and there they are, kissing behind the spotless glass.

Faltered, you look away and back, but it's them for sure, heads too close, mouths greedy for the food and for each other. It's your friend from the French club, the girl he'd call big-boned and shifty. *She's all right when you get to know her,* you'd told him.

Your mother's voice is in your head: *Don't tempt the fates, don't be like me. They'll snatch the hanging fruits away and leave you wanting. One swift boast that life was good, and they took your dad, and I was punished for my flaunting, for laughing in their face.* You should have paid attention, but like a fool you let the light shine in and now the jig is up. At your feet, a man in a ragged parka sits cross-legged on a flattened box, holding up a palm. You envy him the blue tarp, the paperback cracked open on a shabby quilt, his simple dreams of hot soup, chips fresh from the fryer, and a nip of something that'll warm him from the inside. From he who has nothing, surely nothing can be taken.

No one can look ahead in life but if you could, you'd see that you are destined to succeed in every way. If you knew that now, you'd colossus-stride across the street and loom above their avid eyes and laced fingers, you'd make them see you whole, your flesh, your face, your voice – *This is me! Here I am!* But you don't know this yet, still doubting who you are and what you have, still listening to the loop track of your mother's voice. *Mind your step, my girl, and never let them see you smile.* As the beggar looks up like you're his best and only hope, you drop some coins into his grimy hand and turn away with acid leaking from your young, corroding heart.

Water Like A Stone

There's never any actual snow at Christmas, not round here. Sleigh bells, reindeer, the bloody Snowman on the telly, it's all just propaganda for this one dismal day.

I'm invited to daughter's house as per. She's a good kid, but her posh friends witter on about wine and talk in special voices to me, like they're on stage. I want to say you'll be old too one day, you know.

On the way to the bus stop, I nip into the Paki shop for some smokes. You're not supposed to call it that anymore, but old habits die hard. The young fella says, "Happy Christmas, mate," as he hands over my change. I want to ask him, "Is it all as meaningless to you as it is to me?" But no voice comes out.

The cold outside's a punch in the chest. There's a crushed lager can in the dead leaf pile in the bus shelter. No one's about, all indoors with their Yule logs and tinsel. It's like a piece of plywood over a broken window, this day. The real world'll still be there when the sherry wears off.

The driver's wearing a Santa hat. I doze, head against the window, almost miss my stop. Get off, still groggy, and light up a ciggie, that delicious surge of warmth in my lungs. The slagheaps, I call them. Strangely beautiful on the x-ray, like wings. Coal-black frosted with scatterings of white. Not good news of course, no surprise there. Sitting on daughter's garden wall, fighting to catch my breath before knocking, I see a dusting on the pavement, flakes swarming round the streetlights like midges, settling on my sleeve. Well, call me a liar, but there's a first time for everything. And there's also a last.

Old Woman Cooking Eggs, Diego Velasquez, 1618

She feeds the kindling into the hole in her cooking stove and stirs it into flame. It must be hot to make the oil fierce and quick. The sun slices from a high window, striping her copper pot with bars of light, and when she lays a knife across the rim of a white basin, it casts a sharp shadow that she cannot see. She's sent the boy across the river to the garden orchard at the *Alcázar*. The head man, a cousin, lets her have the less than perfect fruit. The boy raced away like the devil was after him, impatient to see the *Flota* that came in yesterday from Veracruz. He's all she has. Her husband died of the pox, her daughter giving birth to the boy. She's 42, won't live too much longer. If he'll only wait. If he'll only stay until her dimming light turns solid black, and he's walked behind her coffin to the *cementerio*. It's all she asks, though she never says the words out loud.

Running full pelt along the rusty streets, he jumps the yellow gutters, dodging beggars' rattling cups and squalls of frantic chickens. The smell of hay and blood from the bullring catches his throat, but his eyes are on the mast tops bristling above the roofs of Triana. On the bridge he stops, avid, breathless, and there they are, lining the quays, low-beamed, long-hulled, sliced with rigging. He breathes deep river silt and the fungal smell of dried tobacco stacked in bales. On the *puerto*, he pushes in among the mariners and merchants, Flemings, Portuguese, Genoese, the tangled languages sounding like song. His feet were made to feel the heave and plunging of the decks, the crunch of Indies sand. He wants to be the one to find the Seven Cities he's heard the sailors talk of, where every temple, tree, and tower drips with gold, more glorious than the Aztecs and the Incas put together. He wants to stand wide-legged on the prow of his *galeón* riding up the river from Cádiz, searching for her milky eyes among the crowd, her face rigid with pride.

The meal is almost ready, a row of sardines on a plate, peeled slices of *jamón* and manchego, a dish of olives flecked with *rocío del mar*. She sits by the crackling stove, listening to time drop its petals one by one around her chair, the eggs held loosely in her hands. As he springs across the threshold, cradling a scarface melon in his arms, she cracks the eggs and drops them in the spitting oil, and, even though she cannot see, she knows how fast the phelgmy whites will thicken, curl, and brown.

Manao Tupapau

When you first saw the Frenchman's paint-stained clothes and hooded eyes, you hid behind your mother's legs, but she gave you to him with an eager push, wanting you to birth a *popa'a's* child. He strapped you on his horse and brought you here and drove his sharp thing up between your legs until you bled. But now the skin down there is thick as footsoles, and he buys you copper earrings from the peddler and weaves you *reva reva* garlands, and when he pounds and grinds, coloured dust rises in the air and you laugh.

In the boldness of the morning, when he left for Papeete to pick up his letters, you washed the calabashes in the river, swept the sand from the mats, and squatted on the veranda to wait. The sun dropped into the lagoon like a falling tree but still he didn't come. Face down naked on the bed, darkness wrapped tight around your head like skin on skin, you listen for the crunch of the Frenchman's step on the grass, craving the sour warmth of his body, the scratch and flare of sulphurous light in his yellow hands. Without him, every shiver of the palms is the creep of lions, the beat of winged beasts with claws to pierce you like a fruit. Without him, a snake lashes on the earthen floor and the *tupapau* draw close, their cold breath against your ear, the spectres of the island come to take you home.

The More Things Change

As the dancing gets wilder, I slip outside for a smoke. Under a bare bulb, by a rank and fermenting wheelie bin, I light up, longing to take off my fancy shoes.

He comes after me as I knew he would. I hand him my ciggie, lipstick-marked, and he takes a long pull.

"That kind of day?" I ask.

"You could say that."

"Lovely service."

He hands the ciggie back. "Bit of a blur to be honest."

"Your mum looks happy."

"As a pig in shit."

"Women and weddings, eh? Who can explain it?"

He looks away, towards the car park. "Not you."

Smoke so deep in my lungs it burns. "No. Not me."

He turns to go inside, back to his waiting bride, then pauses.

"Next week? Usual place?"

I drop the ciggie onto the wet concrete where it flares and dies. I nod.

"I'll be there."

The Birth of the Baptist

Slide the 100 lire coin into the slot. Watch the lights flare and the fresco spring to life, Ghirlandaio's pinks, blues, and greens. Watch your girl in denim shorts stare upward, lips parted, eyes roaming over the ancient stone wall. See her smile at St. Elizabeth reclining, at the wet nurse suckling the infant John the Baptist. And when the coin runs out and the chapel snaps back into darkness, know that you too are just the forerunner, that one day she'll leave you in your own private wilderness with the taste of locusts and wild honey bitter in your mouth.

On Warren Ward

When I tell my grandmother I've been drinking the gin she keeps in her pantry, she squeezes my hand. That's how I know she's still in there, behind the ramparts of that twisted body. We both know death is coming. It's why I'm here.

She sleeps most of the time, but her dark eyes open as the nurse tips her gently to ease the soiled pad from between her legs.

"Hello, Annie, my lovely. Don't you fret. We'll have you looking like a picture in a jiffy."

Bridie in the corner bed died today. Her daughter passed by us, a ratty Kleenex pressed to her nose. Her husband nodded to me as they left the ward, "It's a struggle, int it?"

They are birthing their own endings, these women, in this shabby, beige room, riding waves of pain, confusion, denial. When Ethel needs to pee, she calls high like a bird, "Queek, queek!" From behind the curtain, a nurse says, "Ethel, what's your hand doing down there?" From the next bed, Clarissa calls out, "I've got me boots on. Someone take me boots off." All day long she drapes her extra blanket over her Zimmer frame, then pulls it off, over and over.

Doris in the bed beside us broke her hip when she blacked out in her home. Her husband shuffles in every afternoon, the stains of lunch on his tie. He asks her, "Did nurse do your ears for you today?"

"What?"

"I said, did she do your ears today?"

"Can't hear you."

"Oh, never mind."

A moment of silence.

"She did my ears for me today."

"You daft beggar, I just asked you that."

Doris takes a friendly interest in me. She asks where I've come from – "Ooh, that's a long way" – and asks about a husband and children I cannot come up with. She nods towards the bed where my grandmother lies, toothless mouth open on the pillow.

"They get like that, don't they? They let themselves go."

If you call two strokes and a long, hard life letting go. A chilblained, gas-masked, penny-pinching struggle of a life. Ninety years, give or take.

Nurses bring me tea in cups that smell of disinfectant. They touch my shoulder as they pass. Under the fluorescent lights, time is transparent. The hands of the clock take forever to move from one black digit to the next, yet hours are swallowed whole in the long pauses between each of my grandmother's noisy breaths. She is the flesh of my flesh, the bones of my bones. As darkness fills up the long windows, the ladies shift and mumble in their sleep, dreaming of flying, while I sit on a hard plastic chair, keeping vigil for the fallen.

Siren

In the wet slap of the haar, the lassies slit the herring mouth to tail and pack them into briny barrels. I see her head move among the rest, brown curls escaping from her shawl. She has the juice of silver fishes in her veins – it's in the raised blue of her wrists, her raw fingers, in the taste of oysters when I lick her down below, her skirt canted up and knees apart.

They say despair can be a man's making, but that's not how it feels to me. I give her everything I have – primrose plants, stockings, greenhouse fruits – and everything I am, a stiff-collared man behind a counter at the bank. She says my palms smell of money and loves their smoothness on her skin, but then she sees the brown sails coming, the lads home from the draves, swaggering in their thigh-high boots. She rests her elbows on the bar, pink mouth open, as this one tells of breaching humpbacks and that one tells of waves the height of mountains. I loathe their muckled arms and sunburnt faces and wish them at the bottom of the sea.

She knows the only times I venture out are on the calmest days, sometimes to cast a line and once a year to watch the puffins hatch. It's not an epic life, not one likely to inspire the poets. But when the *Reaper* goes down with all hands lost, it's my door she comes to and cleaves herself to me from head to heel. She says, "I need a man who willnae leave me wantin." Afterwards, cross-legged on the bed, she hangs a pair of cherries over her ear and, giddy with my unexpected luck, I take them in my mouth, stones and all.

Madonna and Child with Apocalypse: a Triptych

Left

With a whoosh and thud, he lands on the courtyard wall, and I leap up, startled, my book flying off my lap. His wings are twin arcs of pure light, and he smells of wet leaves and burnt umber. It's a mystery to me, who he is and where he's come from.

Hands on my chest to calm myself, I bid him welcome.

"Greetings," he says, and I catch a hint of dead mouse on his breath. A shaft of sun cradles a lily in a yellow pot, and in the distance, the tak-tak-tak of gunshots sets the wild dogs howling. I sink back onto my chair, reach for my fallen book, and wait for him to tell me why he's here.

Right

It's a steep and stony climb up from the oasis, and she keeps having to stop to retch up gluey strings of bile so the others go on without them. There's a sheer drop from the edge of the path. The spated river at the bottom of the gulch sounds a long way down. When night closes in, she and her new husband lie against the red rocks, and he says he'll listen out for bandits and soldiers so she can rest. He's a good man. He didn't ask for any of this. North of the Wadi, the rockets are firing, and in the curve of his arms, she watches the green and red stars arc across the sky.

Centre

The baby is fussy, won't suck. His face crumples and twitches, and you stare at it like you're memorizing the moon, the long eyelashes gummy with sleep, a scatter of milk spots, the star of the fontanelle. His tiny penis gushes, and you dab him dry with a handful of sappy grass. Once again you squeeze your nipple between two fingers and graze it on his lips. His mouth pulses once, twice, and as he latches on, that sharp sweet pain, whites turn black and blacks white. You pull him off your breast, and as his screams rise with the curling crown of cloud, burgeoning and topping out, you wrap your long cloak tight around you both, the colour of the sky before the black rain falls.

The Yet Unknowing World

From the bending willow's grasp, she slides into the river. Eyes to the sky, she floats downstream, opens her mouth and sings.

Good morrow, 'tis Saint Valentine's day,
All in the morning betime,
And I a maid at your window,
To be your Valentine.

Borne by her skirt's twin billows, she sings of the fickleness of Princes, of he who called her celestial, his soul's idol, sending her letters drenched with longing, "Doubt thou the stars are fire, Doubt that the sun doth move, Doubt truth to be a liar, but never doubt I love."

Words that gave him leave to slide his arm around her waist, to kiss her neck under the heavy hair that floats around her now, mossy with crow-flowers and dead men's fingers. But all too soon love turned to ashes in his mouth, and he called her bawd and wanton, as a riddling madness drove his mind to fever and his hand too quick to the sword. One thrust, and her father's blood, a waxen pool of scarlet, seeped up the arras like a blush.

And he is dead and gone, laydee, he is dead and gone,
At his head the grass-green turf,
At his heels a stone.

As a bird in sleep, her sodden garments fold around her, the sweet green blur bruising to gentle black, and she's weightless, stoppered, drifting and easeful as a babe in the womb. Yet as she sinks, she's torn up through the river's skin, and the air's a blade in her chest. Bones laid out on the chill, hard ground, she's gripped by a violent shivering.

"Sweet maid, you live."

Her eyes open. Women chafe her feet, wring water from her hair. Above her kneels the Queen, her face a woeful moon.

"Oh Ophelia, you were to be my Hamlet's bride – I would not let you drown."

There's not air enough to speak, river ooze still lodged in the clefts of her lungs.

"I'll have my women bear you to the nuns. They'll nurse you back to your wits and, when you're well, they'll put you on a ship to England."

England. Pennants snapping from great stone castles, hairy-legged horses pawing the peaty ground.

"I pray you, when you reach those foreign shores, tell the world of everything you've seen these days, every carnal act and casual slaughter, even those that were my own. The sands are running out for me, but you, Ophelia, can live to write the sorry tale. I beg you for the sake of him we love."

The Queen bends close to hear her answer. Voiceless yet, Ophelia unfurls a trembling finger to a point, and in the pliant river mud she writes "I Will."

NEW WORLD

Nighthawks

She slips onto the next stool, lips as red as her dress.

"Buy me a cuppa coffee, Mister?"

I tip my hat and nod to the boy behind the counter. The urn spits and steams. He stares at her breasts as he sets the cup down, his acne raw under the fluorescents.

There's a whisper of silk on silk as she crosses her legs. She holds up the coffee to warm her face, though the day's heat lingers, even at the witching hour. A lone car passes up Greenwich Avenue. I offer her a Marlboro, but she shakes her head.

"You got any dough?"

I reach in my pocket and hand her a fold of greenbacks, no questions asked. She holds it up in the fingers of one hand, then looks out through the plate glass window to where someone stands watching, his cigarette glowing in the hot feral night.

Alien

Reilly's in a cab speeding away from JFK, the wipers carving crescents in the dirty windscreen. The driver can't stop talking.

"Staten Island over there? That was my beat when I was with the police department."

"Oh yeah?"

Above the highway, the Kerry hills recede behind a dimpled glass of Jamesons. It's almost midnight in London, too late to call. Reilly sees the phone ringing into the empty air, the bedcover smooth and tight as an ice field.

"It's not a bad life. But then I moved to corrections, what we call a juice move. Not many people want that job, but the pay sure makes the grade."

Across the river, Manhattan rises like an ancient forest. What if he and Laura moved here, to an apartment high above one of those avenues that slice the island north to south. Not a good place to raise children, he thinks, then remembers her eyes in the bathroom mirror, the white stick in her hand.

"In the force, me and my partner, Tony, we did some crazy stuff. Tony was the wild one, I just followed. Two collars a night quota, you know how easy that is? Pick up a coupla punks on a street corner and, how do you like that, they're carrying dope."

Beyond the tunnel, dusk has fallen. Lights swoop from tower to tower across the Brooklyn Bridge. There is no living language for all that Reilly needs to say.

On 46th Street he hands three twenties to the guy, who pulls away without a word. A wind cuts down the narrow street, and he feels it to his bones. The hotel lobby casts a golden glow, but Reilly's rooted to the sidewalk as the Times Square lights skitter through the sky like messages from space.

Triangle

Even in the womb, Mother said, Giulia and I twined round each other like fish in a barrel. Born just thirteen minutes apart, we slept heart to heart in the same bed, warming our feet between each other's calves.

Her face was mine, except for the scar above her eyebrow from when she fell on the fender as a baby. We wore our hair in the same long braid so no-one on the Bowery knew which of us was which.

Everything we did, we did together. Dripping hot candle wax on our fingertips to harden them for the sacks full of garments Mrs. Leventhal brought every day. Scratching our names with a pin on the side of the mantel when no one was looking. When Mother sent us out to the fire escape to peel potatoes, we'd drop the eyes onto the horses' heads and talk about who we'd marry, craning to stare at the Russian boys with the wide black hats and long dark curls down their faces.

Whatever happened on the street or in the family, we knew it all. We knew Mother was done after having Santino, Rosetta, and Angelo in just five years.

When Papa came home from building mansions on the Upper East Side, she'd turn her back as he washed his bare chest in a basin by the stove. Sometimes he'd go out late and not come back all night. We were sure he had another family over by the bridge till we saw him coming out of Ma Rozzoli's whorehouse. When he'd scratch himself through his breeches, we'd bend our heads over our sewing, red-faced with hidden laughter.

Nothing ever came between Giulia and me till Vicenzo Romano. Vic. Yellow-haired, green-eyed, full red lips. He was the stock boy at Benedetti's Delicatessen where I worked at the register. Behind the towering wheels of parmesan, he kissed me, his mouth dusty with the peanuts he liked to chew, splitting them at the seam with his thumbnail.

Giulia was working in a loft shop up near Washington Square Park. On my days off, I waited for her under the sooty trees, pigeons pecking round the toes of my boots. Sometimes Vic came with me and he'd walk us both home. When Ma invited him for supper, I saw Giulia bend to smell his hair as she took his plate. That night under the quilt she asked, "Do you love him, Fina?" but I turned away blushing in the dark.

When Vic bought me a red velvet ribbon, we were as good as engaged. We'd roam the streets at dusk, stopping to kiss just beyond the light cast by store windows. Giulia went about with her friends from the factory. I'd leave the lamp burning for her and wake as she slipped into bed and turned her back to mine.

One night when she came home, I waited up and gave her my ribbon. I knew how much she'd wanted it, how she'd touched the velvet with one wary finger when she thought I didn't see. She took it without a word. When I woke the next morning, she'd already left for work, leaving it coiled loosely on the dresser, a splash of flame in the dim brown room. Leaving it for me. Running the soft velvet between thumb and finger, I made two loops of it and tied them in a bow.

Later, Vic and I walked to meet Giulia from her shift, weaving through the almost evening crowd, dodging the soft green turds dropped by the dray horses, breathing the vegetable stink of the gutter. As we strolled the pathways of the park, March rawness made me clutch Vic's arm close. A clatter of heels and a woman ran by us, then a patrolman wheeled his horse towards thick black smoke pulsing across the skyline. From Giulia's building.

High above us, faces crowded the blazing windows, mouths open. Fire horses skittered, eyes white, a hose slithered across the asphalt and a ladder cranked up and up, with a great groaning, then stopped – "Too short!" – and women wailed and screamed and covered their eyes. Girls clinging to window frames launched like a flock of birds, raining down on the asphalt in a drumroll of moist thuds.

A girl balanced on a sill, up on her toes. Even from afar, I saw the red circle round her neck. Arms raised high, muscles of fire arcing from her shoulders, she leaned gently forward and fell, sparks cartwheeling from the ends of her hair.

Wrenching myself from Vic's grasp, I ran, seeing nothing, hearing nothing but Vic behind me calling "Fina!" Up the tenement stairs, past women leaping to their feet in an avalanche of cloth, I raced to our cold dark bedroom, snatched the ribbon from the dresser and fell to my knees.

"It wasn't her, it wasn't her!"

But when I turned to look at Vic, when I saw his mouth twitch and his eyes dart, I knew that Giulia had her own ribbon, as red as mine and just as soft between the fingers.

I'm 90 years old now and the people here are very kind. They move the mirror with me from the chair to the bed and back. They know I like to talk to Giulia. It's like it always was for us, there's no one else we need. I no longer see her scar. It's sunk into the fretwork of our ancient face, those lines I trace all day and night, my finger on the cold unyielding glass.

Snow Falling Upwards

Meteorology man, you called me when you first learned of my weakness for weather. My love for fire rainbows and sun dogs. For lake effect snow and katabatic winds.

"Weather is mood, and climate is personality," I'd tell you as you tugged the shirt from my waistband. "As for snow falling upwards, it's just a trick of the wind and the eye. Gravity will always make it fall."

There's a photograph of you lying on our seagrass rug, listening to Satie's *Gymnopédies*, a sunbeam striped across your waist. You did bliss very well. In our thousand days together, you'd always listen like you were hearing music, even when it was just my voice, full of unnecessary language.

Over the years, I thought of our lives as railroad tracks, moving forward side by side but never touching. Sometimes I could taste the want of you, but then I'd think about sleeping dogs and Pandora's box. Instead, I stalked the high latitudes for the greening pulse of the auroras, my wife holding the receiver to catch their eerie sighs and whistles. When she died, I said, "Soon," but first there was the paperwork, a sorting through, and the four stages, a long tunnel with damp and crumbling walls. Only then did I send the letter drafted long ago, folded into clean, white thirds.

This is what I do, I wait too long. I'd imagined you in a wooden house in the mountains with a great lake spreading out from your door, but now I know there's not a single place on earth I'd find your footprint. I only hope the spheres are making music where you are. Here, there's nothing but a goitered winter moon and the slow drag of an ice circle turning in the dark.

Janus

In Macy's one Saturday afternoon, as I'm looking through the sale racks, I glance up and see his wife. I know it's her because I'd snuck a look at the picture in his wallet when he was in the shower. She has a strong face, not the kind you forget. Definitely not an apologetic kind of face.

She's heaping clothes onto the counter, pointing out a mislabeled price to the assistant. Her voice carries. A small girl leans back, bored, against her mother's coat. Gracie. Five years old. Another child in a stroller, a wool hat sliding back off his shiny hair, turning his head to follow the people walking by. Simon. Two and a half. His children. Their children.

As the assistant keys her purchases into the register, the wife taps her credit card on the counter and gazes in my direction. I stare hard at the shiny row of hanger tops in front of me. When I dare look back, she's wheeling the stroller away, two large Macy's bags hanging from the handles. Gracie follows, her feet dragging. They pass the purse display and weave through the maze of cosmetic counters near the door. Gracie looks up at a woman on a stool getting a makeover, and a bright red mitten drops from her pocket onto the polished floor.

In the sudden noise of the street, the wife is bending to pull Simon's hat down around his ears.

"Excuse me," I say, holding out the mitten.

The wife straightens up.

"Oh, that's Grace's. Did she drop it?"

I nod, dumb with grief. She takes the mitten and smiles at me.

"She's always losing them. I should string them through her coat like my mother used to do. Thanks a lot."

"No problem."

I turn to go.

"Say thank you to the lady, Grace."

I turn back. The traffic noise swells inside my head. The little girl looks up, frowning, and those blue-gray eyes, startlingly familiar, see me for exactly what I am.

Abby and the Astronaut

Abby was in the Air and Space Museum looking at a photograph of three young men in bulky space suits grouped around an enormous Presidential seal. Only one of them could really be called handsome, with a sculpted jaw and eyes as blue as oceans seen from space. Aware of someone at her shoulder, Abby turned and found herself looking into that very face. The hair had receded, but there was no mistaking those eyes.

"Hi."

He held out his hand. She shook it.

"Aren't you...?"

"I'm Chuck B. Anderson. I went up in Zephyr III. And who are *you*?"

Chuck wore a turtleneck and a tweed jacket, and his waist was flat above the belt of his chinos. He took Abby to lunch in the glass atrium of the museum's restaurant. Beyond the roar of voices in the echoing space, the Capitol dome levitated in the heat haze. Over their empty salad plates, the Astronaut reached for Abby's hand and pulled gently at the webs of skin between her fingers.

Everywhere in the city there were statues of celebrated men. Abby had taken them all in – Lincoln magisterial on his massive chair, Jefferson in his giant gazebo, handsomer than in life, the long-legged Andrew Jackson on a prancing horse in Lafayette Square, waving his cocked hat at The White House. They even walked the streets in flesh and blood. Pausing with his aides at a crosswalk on the Senate side, Ted Kennedy turned to watch Abby's legs as she walked past, while she tried not to stare at that florid, unmistakable face.

There were no famous people where Abby came from. Whatever happened always happened somewhere else. At night Main Street was deserted. All the streetlamps had to shine on was the row of empty pick-ups outside Erikkson's bar and the metallic walls of Lundgren's creamery, which loomed over the town like an ocean liner in dry dock.

Chuck's apartment was the closest, down near the marina in Southwest. He drove her there in his silver Miata. A fountain ejaculated in the lobby of his building. The elevator was lined with mirrors, and when Abby looked up, she had a bird's-eye view of the crown of his head. It looked rosy but hard, like a nut.

In his apartment, every flat surface held an enormous crystal. Abby picked one up and ran her fingers over its facets.

"What are they supposed to do?" she asked, passing a rock of rose quartz from hand to hand. Chuck took it away from her and put it back on its shelf.

"You can damage their auras if you hold them too long."

In the bedroom, Chuck closed the drapes and lit the candles ranged across his dresser as Abby perched on the edge of the bed, swinging her heels. Shaking out the match, Chuck shrugged off his jacket and came towards her.

As a girl, Abby had dreamed of being ravished by a centaur. She'd raise her legs under the covers and run her hands down the human chest and onto the coarse warmth of the creature's hide. What she'd wanted was to have something mythical between her thighs. Nothing less would do. So when Chuck B. Anderson gently tipped her onto her back, she closed her eyes and let herself be entered by a legend.

Haven

No sooner has Ben driven off down the track when the morning sky turns a bruised yellow-gold and the pitch of the air rises to a sonic hum. Scooter, Ben's lab, slinks head and shoulders under the bed, whining. Above the cabin, 70-foot trees flail and groan. Just one of them falling, Layla knows, would crush it to splinters and turn her body to pulp, her feet stuck out from the wreckage like the Wicked Witch of the East.

She's only here because Ben likes her to try new things. Yesterday they hiked tinder-dry mountain trails where every turn had a Beware of Bears sign. Today Ben's gone to rent kayaks. "You'll love it," he said, though he knows how often she flings upright in bed from dreams of drowning, lungs pancaked, heart jangled. He holds her then, rubbing her shoulders and back, always waiting till her breathing has slowed before pushing her gently downwards.

Darkness falls, the day turned upside down. Niagaras of rain pound the roof, and the high trees whip and crack. Layla sinks to the floor and clings to Scooter's trembling rump. With every flash, she keens through her teeth, bracing for timber. Under her hands, the dog's haunches shift, and in the dark, she feels his wet breath on her ear, his warm bulk pressed against her side.

When Ben gets back with kayaks strapped to the roof of his car, the woods sparkle with sunlit diamonds. Layla is on the porch steps, arms around Scooter's neck, her face in his fur. Scooter, her port in a storm, her knight in shining armor. The only one she's ever known.

This is How You Mourn Your Father

1. Post the news and watch the all-day buzz and shudder of your phone.
2. Pull on a teeshirt fresh from the dryer, *that sharp clean smell.*
3. Search for a last-minute flight that doesn't cost the earth.
4. Write down who he was in the world, the bald and simple facts.
5. *The ring of your boot heels in the airport parking garage.*
6. Buy a paper on the concourse. Relish the heft and flow of the words you chose.
7. Note the rainbow edge of clouds below the plane. Something he taught you, t*he refraction of light.*
8. *The inverted stillness of the house. His watch and glasses, the trailing vacuum of his socks.*
9. Zip up your black dress. *His Hawaiian shirts, his bow ties and cigars, his fragrant whisky breath. The recliner breaking when you climbed in with him one too many times.*

10. Watch the casket slide away. Wait for the bait and switch, his face around the curtain, grinning.
11. Shake hands, lean into one-armed hugs, your glass damp in its napkin. Pick up a deviled egg. Put it down.
12. Watch the PowerPoint loop, boy and dog in black and white, cocksure graduate in gown, groom with bride and cake. Holding a baby you, his beard grasped tight in your seashell fist.
13. *That last call when he'd fallen and you asked him to stop drinking and he got mad which pissed you off because how could you not worry and want to keep him safe, but now you know what he knew and can see that drinking was a fraying rope across a chasm, carving weals into his tender human palms.*

Atropa Belladonna

From three cars back, I see Sadie on the sidewalk outside school, her head bent over her purple phone like always. The Lord only knows how she's my child. Connor looks like his dad and me, solid on his feet, well proportioned. He knows how to fit right in. Never had to teach him – he just knew.

When my turn at the curb comes, Sadie knuckles her glasses up her nose and climbs in back, slotting her seatbelt in one-handed. She doesn't meet my eyes in the rear view.

"Good day?" I ask, putting on my signal to pull out.

No answer, so I say her name like the therapist suggested, and Sadie looks up.

"Nick Botarelli thinks Martin Luther King said give me liberty or give me death. Ha ha. He's as dumb as a brick."

It was one of the Founding Fathers, I know that much.

I've warned her no one likes a smarty-pants. All she does is look up every little fact. I've never seen her take a selfie or even make a call. Once I took the phone away from her for a week, tucked it way back in my pantie drawer to hide that ugly purple, but she didn't speak a single word to me till I gave it back.

"Honey, it's lovely out so I thought let's go by the park and see if the hydrangeas are blooming yet."

Flowers are my thing. I work mornings at a high-end florist, no drug store carnations for us. I'm good at what I do – cutting stems on the diagonal, pinching stamens, stripping birthing petals off the roses. And choosing combinations that are easy on the eye.

I pull into a shady parking spot, and we set off down the dappled path, Sadie in front, shoulders hunched. Even from behind, I can tell she's scrolling. After our plump and lovely little boy (he lost the baby fat eventually), I wanted a girl so bad, and when the doctor put her in my arms, I don't think I've ever been so happy. She had tiny, perfect mother-of-pearl nails, but her shining head was bald for months. I tried every kind of bow, but they always slipped off, and when her hair did finally grow in, it was thin and crisp with static.

Sadie runs to the wooden bridge across the creek and hooks her feet onto the bottom rail so she can throw twigs down into the moving water. I want to shape her face with my hands, smooth out the nose, pinch the cheekbones, press her mouth on either side to plump her lips. She's laid the phone down on the railing, and that shriek of purple against the soft mossy green of the trees hurts my eyes. She looks away, and one flick of a finger's all it takes. As the phone plummets, she lunges for it, but I grab my daughter's waistband and hold on for dear life.

Resting Place

Quick as knives, a hand across your mouth, an elbow on your throat, you're dragged behind a fallen tree. Legs thrash on crunchy leaves, his, yours, his sour breath, the smell of dirt and sweat, a gripping on your neck till stars and darkness come, then you're broken open, riven raw and burning. He slams into you three, four times, your head cracked on the rooted earth, then all at once he's done and scrabbles up and goes.

Your breath's a saw-toothed rasping, your wild eyes inches from the deadwood fungus scurrying with ants. Trying to rise, you catch the lake's shimmy and a notice flapping on a tree, but then a drag of razor wire from ear to ear sinks you down onto the black and sticky ground.

Blades and thorny tangles stir, the bleachy undersides of leaves, and flies are loops and lines of light. A helicopter growls across the sky from right to left, invisible above the trees. A twig cracks, and the air turns jagged red until you spot the deer, its eyes wide to the metal tang, the smell of what's in your mouth, behind your teeth, beneath your tongue. There's static in your loamy brain so when a robin shrills its piercing notes a dozen times, you long to club it to a flattened mess of claws and feathers.

You know the two ways this could end. Perhaps there'll be the sound of running footsteps, a kneeling in the clotted grass, hip-held radios crackling, and then the rush of sunlit treetops through the blued-out window. Then again, there may be only this – the cathedral sway of timbers, a long slow greying of the light, and, somewhere in the jungle grass, the furtive, watchful circling of wolves.

Jericho Road

The first time I see them he's beating her head against the roof of his car.

I'm in the kitchen making coffee when I hear it, a rhythmic thud thud thud. I'm taking a break, the long transcription two-thirds done, still in my pj bottoms and a sweatshirt with a hole in the elbow. The percolator bubbles and hisses. Waiting, I drift into the living room and stroke the cat, who's stretched out on the sofa like a flying monkey. I hear it again, the thud thud thud, and another noise I can't place, a kind of keening. I look out the bay window between the security bars, and half a block up Constitution there they are.

I'm out in the street before I know it, barefoot on the hot pavement.

"Hey!"

The man, tall, slim, well-dressed, turns his head and glares. He has her face pressed sideways against the metal roof.

"Let her go!"

I hesitate just outside my gate. What if he has a gun?

"I'm calling the cops. Right now!"

Then I realize my phone is inside.

"Ma'am, run over here. Come here to my house. Get away from him."

His fist in her hair is twisted so tight her eyes are slanted.

"Not your business, lady."

He doesn't shout but his voice carries. The woman gestures at me, a waving away. Am I making things worse? Again her head smacks against metal, hard.

A cop car – no siren – swings up 10th and pulls up to the curb. Someone must have called. The man lets go the woman's hair but grabs her wrist.

Jeri from across the street hurries over.

"You okay, hon?"

"Did you see that? In broad daylight! I tried to get her to come to me, but she wouldn't. I didn't know what else to do."

"Sweetie, that kind of woman won't listen to reason."

DC's finest get out like they have all the time in the world. One pats the man down and then walks him to the corner. The man's hands are raised, palms out, like he's saying, "It's all good, officer. Just a misunderstanding." The other cop, his notebook out, talks to the woman. She bends low over her crossed arms and shakes her head at every question he asks.

The officers confer, then drift towards their cruiser.

"She's sending them away? I don't believe it."

The woman moves round to the passenger side of the car, smoothing her hair. The morning sun spotlights the place on the roof where her face was pressed, filmed with skin cells and sweat and DNA. As she gets in the car, she shoots me a look under her brows, hostile, strangely triumphant.

"Oh my god, what is her problem? He could have killed her."

Jeri shakes her head.

"It's a sickness, hon. They can't help themselves. I pray they don't have children. They're the ones I feel bad for."

The next time I see them they're sitting at a bar, wound around each other, her long shiny legs rubbing up against his.

It's a Friday night at Rumors downtown. I'm with a bunch of people from a client company, a happy hour that turned into a night out. I lean way back in my chair to get a better look. It's definitely them. He caresses a long curl of her hair like he's fingering expensive fabric. She's laughing with him, fitted into the curve of his body.

Between the churning dancers, I watch them. When she slides off her bar stool, I follow her into the ladies' room. In my stall, I scribble my phone number on the back of a CVS receipt I've found in my wallet.

Just ten digits and two initials – nothing else. When I hear her flush, I come out and lean into the mirror right next to her. Her eyes flick to my face and then away. No sign of recognition.

A cluster of girls bursts into the ladies' room, shrieking and slamming stall doors, shouting and laughing over the partitions. I have the note in my hand. She presses her lips together to set her gloss. As she pushes back a curve of hair, there's a greenish half-moon over her brow, and again I see the man's hands in her hair, the white knuckling of his grip, and the look on her face as she got into the car. A look that said, "Back off, bitch. You know nothing."

I push the note back into my purse and reach in front of her – "Excuse me" – to pump the soap dispenser. As I'm waving my hands beneath the faucet sensor, she turns on her high heels and leaves the bathroom. The laughing girls crowd up to the sinks, a miasma of perfume, hair spray, and alcohol breath. I look into my eyes in the mirror and wring my hands under the sudden rush of water.

Consanguinity

Vicodin has clenched my bowels into a fist. I grip the toilet roll holder and brace for one last burning push and, when I stand to strap on a fresh maxi-pad, a clot drops to the tiles, viscous and oily. I wipe it up with a handful of toilet paper but leave the crime scene splatter on the wall for Guy to deal with later.

The rubber bedsheet is cold on my legs, but the muggy air from the window makes me sweat so I turn the pillow over to the cool side. It smells of unwashed hair. Outside, a kid is beating on a trash can, and, every time a car goes by, the dog across the street bursts into a frenzy of barking. I slide the window shut and listen to the blood pool inside me, strident as a rusty nail, sighing in my ears, my neck, my wrists, a seashell sound, surging in the pad whenever I roll over. Three tries at IVF, then Guy was done. He said we have a good life, let's not waste it. We've walked the Great Wall, waded knee-deep in Patagonian penguins, drifted in a hot air balloon across a bleached south-western sky. In each new place, I've lain my palms on my belly and felt it riding high, drum-tight and jumping like a cricket.

The continent inside me is bosky, uncharted. In a week they'll snip and carve and scoop, they'll split the green earth open at the source and leave a scar so raw it can be seen from space. Swaddled in a sheet, I feel the mattress dip beneath Guy's weight, the hunger in his hands, the urge to grip and pull me, fists clenched and crusty-eyed, out into the unrelenting light.

Lepidopterae

You're in the parking lot above the lake when your phone rings, and you stare at the screen a while before answering. They never call from the nursing home except when things are bad. *Your mom's not responding, can't be woken, you might want to come.* You hang up and walk the dirt track to the water's edge, the place where you like to come to drain off the stress of the working day, and as you look out across the glassy shimmer, your ancestors rise in a lacy cloud and settle on your arms, chest, and head.

This is new.

When you first came here, they never paid you any mind, just flittered around the gator-looking log where they like to bask or dipped their heads into the joe-pye weed, but this time they mean business. You can tell from the sticky whisper of their feet on your skin. Here's your Mee-maw who had a minor stroke at 55 and stayed in her lounger for 30 years waiting for another. Your two gay uncles, one forever in the closet, and one who did Pride every year in full drag and let you wear his rainbow wig. Aunt Flora, bitten by a rabid dog who she'd caught lapping foamy-mouthed from her kiddie pool. Your father, who taught you how to change a tire and shoot a BB gun, he's here too for old times' sake, having left when you were 13 for a sexy widow whose daughter had your exact same name.

Even the babies are here, the ones your mom couldn't carry to term. You wish they'd lived. From everything you've seen, there's safety in numbers. You're the first and only port of call, but Mom's always said you put your own needs before hers. Sure, you moved away, but when her second husband left and she showed up on your doorstep with a roller case and her own comforter, you took her in and fed her one bite at a time like a baby. You'd get home from work and smell the wine before your key was in the door. And when she married the next guy, you never told her how he'd always find a way to grab your ass two-handed when you'd show up on holidays with fruit baskets and baked goods.

And now there's a deathbed to consider and a trip to the nursing home you really don't want to make. What kind of daughter lets her mother die alone, you ask yourself in a voice that isn't yours. You lift your arms, each one a sleeve of flickering wings, and ask your kin for advice. What's family good for except to tell you what to do? You wait, hands stretched high like a hallelujah, but there's only a soft lapping on your cheeks and behind your ears.

They're multiplying by the minute, so many you have to brush them off the back of your scrubs before getting in the car. As you back out of the spot, you remember your mom going after the neighbor's boy with a hammer when she found him on top of you on the basement couch. There's that. And one time she let you play hooky from school and took you to Denny's for a Grand Slam with milk shakes and extra fries. And before your dad left – it comes back to you as you pull into your driveway – he'd slap her on the butt when she wore slacks, and she'd get all tight-lipped pretending to be mad, and the room felt full of caramel, thick and gummy and holding you in place.

In the end, it's a false alarm, a bad reaction to the amoxicillin your mom was taking for a UTI. The nurse calls again to say she's back to being her ornery self. Medication always did whack her out. Not like you, who needed not one but two shots of Demerol when you tore up your knee. Genes aren't the whole story, but tell that to the ancestors. Weeks later they're still with you in your house, rising and settling as you get on and off the couch, sucking the nectar from your orange peels and the skin of your bananas. Whenever you get home from your shift, they flock to greet you. They seem to think you need the company. Truth is, you're getting used to the smell of rotting fruit and the sight of chrysalises hula-hooping from the ceiling, each one pulsing like a sturdy beating heart.

The Few, The Proud

There were only 60 of them on the aircraft carrier to 5,000 of us sailors, but they were tough sons-of-bitches and I'd back them against any mutiny.

When we came into port, we were shipped ashore for liberty. White hats thronging the streets, knocking back *sake*, barfing in the gutters. Pity the poor locals. Marines and seamen got into fights made your bones rattle just watching. A kid named Prentice, real white-bread, middle-class, told us some crazy-ass dude bit off a chunk of his hand in Yokosuka. I saw the bandage but didn't believe him.

Months later I was shooting the breeze with a Marine while I was polishing the railings outside the Captain's office. The guy flipped open his wallet and showed me a shriveled strip of gray flesh – the missing piece of Prentice's hand. I was blown away – "I know that guy!" Big ship, small world. Moral – don't mess with a Jarhead. Never felt safer in my life.

A Still, Small Point of Reference

Each morning as the egg-yolk sun rises down the beach, I see you start your vigil, coffee cup in hand, staring out to where the sea's a silver dazzle, where every whitecap, every diving bird deceives the eye.

As the days stretch their arc across the water, I watch you watching the horizon, your feet up on the railing, binoculars around your neck. Since I first kissed you long ago in freshman year, I've learned to love your doggedness, the torque of it, the thing that drives you on when other people fall away.

But I see how much you miss in all that striving. The ebbing surf on the tight wet sand edged with tiny bubbles. The jerky strut of sandpipers. Humming insects in the dune grass, and the dart of lizards on sun-warmed wood. The taste of salt against your mouth, the sweet drag of fingertips on peeling summer skin.

Even on that epic day when they crested close to shore, even as you ran along the beach beside them and felt a sonic pulse of kinship pass from them to you and back again, it was over just as soon as it began. As the pod outpaced your human stride, the black fins dwindling down the shore and out of sight, you were left with nothing but the long waves frilling around your ankles, already wanting more.

The Chemistry of Living Things

The blue ones make me dream of thistles, make me loop-de-loopy, shaking bubbles from my wrists. The big yellow ones are slow-witted and tip me into drenching sleep at unexpected hours. The white diamonds have a certain easy charm, but it's the tiny silver ones I like the best. In my cupped palm they roll like mercury balls, but in my head they fizz and dazzle, splintering into gaudy reds and greens. They're the reason I can glide above the broken glass, put a soft hand on my husband's shoulder as he tells our guests another story and nods to me to bring the coffee and dessert. Smoke coils beneath the lamp, softening the light. The faces round the table seem familiar, but I don't know who they are, the men with bristled hair, the women oiled and shiny with cat's-eye glasses and wet teeth. Mouths open, voices bourbon-loud with the looseness of late evening. The noise pulls close around my head like curtains as I rinse the dirty plates and spear a perfect sprig of mint in every peach sorbet. Against the backsplash, the pill bottles gleam, and I promise-touch each one for later. You and you and you. Through the window, just beyond the house-thrown light, a young deer stares at me with deep, black eyes. I see its dappled hide, a white stripe on its haunch that may or may not be a scar. I know at once it's come to lure me out into the dark and unfamiliar, onto bleak, untrodden ground. I press my hands five-fingered on the window, and, when I wipe away the cloud my breath has made, the deer has gone like it was never there at all.

World Enough

That week.

As I turn the calendar from May to June, I'm staggered by a rising tide of memories from back before the flood. Lifting the shiny page and piercing it through the nail, that week's here again, the sudden heat after days of chilly rain, your wife and kids at the beach while you stayed home to decorate the house. Showing up on my doorstep at midnight, naked beneath your paint-stained jeans, rumpled, ripe, and hard. All-night sprawls in the trodden sheets, your fingers in my grooves and empty spaces, your teeth on the back of my neck, the swoon of it, making me come from behind. Afterwards, eating beans from the can, passing it from hand to hand. Your wince when an orange bean dropped on the sheet, your grin as I slid low and licked it up with a lizard tongue still tasting of you. And waking to the clash and grind of the garbage truck through the wide-flung windows and you, sleepy-eyed and keys in hand, already halfway gone.

It's twelve years on, a good man and three kids later, and a breast sewn shut like a smile. This year's

June is scored with crosses marking time. On the kitchen counter, shiny with the bleach wipes we've been told to use, a basket brims with prescription bottles with childproof caps, and the cat's a pretzel curl on the basket chair in the sun, dreaming of nothing but now. Through the long windows, I watch my children playing softball in the yard, the grass long worn to dust, the baby – no, he's four years old – looking upward as he runs, on his face the endless hope that this time he'll catch the ball and hold it tight enough to last.

The Shape of Things to Come

Karen's on her tummy by the edge of the pond, watching Opa feed the koi. They zig and zag under the lily pads in tangles of orange and yellow. The sun's hot on the back of her neck, and the grass pricks her skin through her bathing suit.

Her Oma sits in a lawn chair, smoking a cigarette, the cubes in her iced tea tinkling when she sips.

"Tell my fortune, Oma."

Karen's palm is dwarfed in the cradle of her grandmother's wide hand. With the tip of one nail, Oma traces the lifeline, and a tickly feeling runs all the way down Karen's back.

"You'll have a long happy life with lots of children. And a good man to take care of you."

It's what she always says.

"Will there be horses?"

"Yes, Schatzi, there'll be all the horses you could wish for. Now go play while I make lunch."

Turning cartwheels through the ragged grass, Karen maps her own future. There'll be a large ranch house with long windows to the floor. She's already drawn it in an exercise book, one boxy room after another, furnished with pictures cut out of her mother's magazines – long low couches, round purple cushions, a glass coffee table. There'll be four children – two boys and two girls – and a shadowy husband who carries a briefcase and isn't home much.

Her Oma calls "Picnic!" and Karen runs to the patio to a tuna salad sandwich on a paper plate. The umbrella lays stripes of shadow across the table. A pop as Oma opens a Coke. Karen holds her finger over the neck of the bottle, feeling the straw push up against her finger. Oma shakes out some chips from the big crinkly bag onto her plate. Their crunch against the soft sweetness of the bread is the usual delight in her mouth.

In two years, her father will leave and move to California with a new wife. Her mom will take Karen to live in New Jersey where she'll work as a secretary in a lawyer's office. Except for Christmas cards, they'll mostly lose touch with her father's parents in Minnesota. Karen will lose her virginity in 11th grade to a boyfriend who hates to wear condoms, so she'll sweat bullets every month till her period comes. There'll be no money for college so Karen will go work in city government in Newark, first as a typist and later in data entry. She'll meet a nice man there,

Rolf, and they'll marry, but there'll be no children, and she'll come to see there'd never been any need for condoms. She and Rolf will work hard, saving enough to buy a one-story house on a nice street. There'll be good times with neighbors, evenings in the yard with beers in the cooler and citronella candles lit, fireflies popping in the trees. Trips to Florida, driving all night, then walking on the beach in St. Pete in the setting sun, pelicans skimming just above the waves on their pterodactyl wings. Collecting shells for her mantel at home, the home they'll lose to foreclosure when Rolf is laid off just exactly as Karen's mother shows the first signs of Alzheimer's. Her mom will fret and pace the confines of their apartment till one day she'll fall on the cold bathroom tile, the beginning of the end. Then the gun lap, Rolf going first, an aneurysm in the street, then Karen's own body ossifying limb by limb till she stops even trying to move. She'll spend her last days and nights on the couch, drifting in and out of sleep, watching the birds peck at the empty feeder beyond the living room window till there's nothing left for her to see.

But on this summer's afternoon in 1964, there's just the dandelion-seed air drifted with bees, and her Oma cheering as Opa turns on the sprinkler and Karen runs round and round through the rainbowed spray, laughing like there's no tomorrow.

Acknowledgements

First and foremost, my deepest thanks to Jude Higgins at Ad Hoc Fiction for publishing *The Yet Unknowing World* and for being such an indispensable driving force in the world of flash fiction. Her weekly Ad Hoc Fiction micro competition was the reason I got into writing flash in the first place, and it has been a joyous ride ever since thanks to the camaraderie and support of my worldwide network of talented writing buddies. You know who you all are!

Many grateful thanks also to all of the following people: John at Ad Hoc Fiction for his excellent production skills. The extraordinary creative force that is Florence Clementine for her beautiful cover design. Keith Donohue, Kathy Fish, Annemarie Neary, Nuala O'Connor, and Meg Pokrass for their generous and insightful words about the collection. Andrew Mackintosh, my webmeister extraordinaire and a great brother as well. Jeanette Sheppard for her helpful insights into how to compile a flash collection. The mighty Donohues – Keith for valuable manuscript advice and Melanie for meticulous proofreading. All of the members of my various writing groups over the years who have helped me to grow as a writer, especially my buddy girls Jan Linley and Beth Millemann who have been there for me in more ways than I can ever repay. And eternal thanks to my husband Mike who gives me exactly as much space as I need to write and some cracking material into the bargain.

Previously Published

Grateful thanks to the following anthologies and journals where these pieces were previously published:

A Still, Small Point of Reference – *Hysteria 6 Anthology*, November 2017, and NFFD Flash Flood, June 2018

Abby and the Astronaut – *District Lines II* (anthology of DC writers), Summer 2014

Agape – Retreat West, August 2018

Alien – *To Carry Her Home: Bath Flash Fiction Anthology Volume 1*, Ad Hoc Fiction, February 2017

Atropa Belladona – NFFD Flash Flood, June 2019

Consanguinity – *The Real Jazz Baby: Reflex Fiction Volume 2*, Reflex Press 2019

First Time – Retreat West, February 2016

Haven – Reflex Fiction, May 2018

Hindsight – Winner of the Ad Hoc Fiction Contest, December 2015, and *Flash, I Love You* anthology, Paper Swans Press, December 2017

How Gypsy Jenny Likes to Bathe – *Flash Fiction Festival 3 Anthology*, Ad Hoc Fiction, November 2019

How It Begins – Fictive Dream, February 2018

Ice Harvesting – Spelk Fiction, October 2016

Janus – Gargoyle #64, Spring 2016

Jericho Road – *District Lines III* (anthology of DC writers), January 2016

Latchkey – *A Box of Stars Beneath the Bed: National Flash Fiction Day 2016 Anthology*, Gumbo Press, 2016

Lepidopterae – Ellipsis Zine, August 2020

Madonna and Child with Apocalypse – New Flash Fiction Review, April 2019

Manao Tupapau – *Flash Fiction Festival 2 Anthology*, Ad Hoc Fiction, November 2018

Nighthawks – Winner, Ad Hoc Fiction Contest, January 2016

Old Woman Cooking Eggs, Diego Velásquez, 1618 – *Future Shock Anthology*, Retreat West Books, 2019

On Warren Ward – TSS, November 2015, and NFFD Flash Flood, June 2020

Reign – *Flash, I Love You* anthology, Paper Swans Press, December 2017

Resting Place – *The Lobsters Run Free: Bath Flash Fiction Volume 2*, Ad Hoc Fiction, 2017

Siren – *Things Left and Found by the Side of the Road: Bath Flash Fiction Volume 3*, Ad Hoc Fiction, 2018; *Best Microfiction 2019*, Pelekinesis Press, 2019; and *Best Small Fictions 2019*, Sonder Press, 2019

Snow Falling Upwards – *With One Eye on the Cows: Bath Flash Fiction Volume 4*, Ad Hoc Fiction, November 2019

Sole Survivor – NFFD FlashFlood, June 2017

The Birth of the Baptist – *Ripening: National Flash Fiction Day Anthology 2018*, July 2018

The Cardboard Box of Happiness – Fictive Dream, February 2020

The Chemistry of Living Things – *Fish Anthology 2018*, Fish Publishing, July 2018, and *Best Microfiction 2019*, Pelekinesis Press, 2019

The More Things Change – The Casket of Fictional Delights, August 2016

The Shape of Things to Come – Nottingham Review, March 2017

This Is How You Mourn Your Father – *Barely Casting A Shadow: Reflex Fiction Volume 1*, Reflex Press, 2018

Triangle – Lost Balloon, November 2017

Water Like a Stone – NFFD FlashFlood, June 2016, and *A Cache of Flashes: Worcestershire LitFest Anthology*, November 2016

World Enough – Spelk Fiction, August 2018

About the Author

Fiona J. Mackintosh lives in the suburbs of Washington, D.C. with her husband but grew up in Scotland by the sea and is a citizen of both the U.S. and the U.K. An ex-journalist, she now earns her living as a freelance editor, mainly for the World Bank. Her fiction has been widely published on both sides of the Atlantic. In 2018, she won the Fish Flash Fiction Award, the Bath Flash Fiction Award, and the Reflex Fiction Prize, and her winning stories were selected for Best Small Fictions 2019, Best Microfictions 2019, and BIFFY 50. In 2016, she was honoured to receive an Individual Artist's Award from the State of Maryland. For more details, please follow Fiona on Twitter (@ fionajanemack) or go to: www.fionajmackintosh.com.

Story Index